FORBIDDEN CLASSROOM
THE INTRUDER

Written by Tony Bradman

Illustrated by Dylan Gibson

RISING ★ STARS

ISBN: 9781398324220

Text © 2022 Tony Bradman
Illustrations, design and layout © Hodder and Stoughton Ltd
First published in 2022 by Hodder & Stoughton Limited (for its Rising Stars imprint, part of the Hodder Education Group),
An Hachette UK Company
Carmelite House, 50 Victoria Embankment, London EC4Y 0DZ

www.risingstars-uk.com

Impression number 10 9 8 7 6 5 4 3 2 1
Year 2026 2025 2024 2023 2022

Author: Tony Bradman
Series Editor: Tony Bradman
Commissioning Editor: Hamish Baxter
Educational Reviewer: Helen Marron
Illustrator: Dylan Gibson
Design: Helen Townson
Page layout: Stephanie White/Kamae Design Ltd
Editor: Amy Tyrer

With thanks to the schools that took part in the development of Reading Planet KS2, including: Ancaster CE Primary School, Ancaster; Downsway Primary School, Reading; Ferry Lane Primary School, London; Foxborough Primary School, Slough; Griffin Park Primary School, Blackburn; St Barnabas CE First & Middle School, Pershore; Tranmoor Primary School, Doncaster; and Wilton CE Primary School, Wilton.

A catalogue record for this title is available from the British Library.

Printed in India.

Orders: Please contact Hachette UK Distribution, Hely Hutchinson Centre, Milton Road, Didcot, Oxfordshire, OX11 7HH.
Telephone: (44) 01235 400555. Email: primary@hachette.co.uk

ROCKHEAD PRIMARY SCHOOL FILES

TO: SENTINELS HQ

AGENTS: RIPLEY AND ARNIE

REPORTING IN FROM: ROCKHEAD PRIMARY SCHOOL

Building work on the school has caused a wall to be demolished, revealing the classroom that was sealed off in December 1983.

We have recruited VERNA LEE and JAMIE BALLARD, two Year 6 children in the school, who realised that something was going on.

They have convinced the headteacher, MRS SHARMA, that they are turning the Forbidden Classroom into a special project. This means they can now work undercover.

The portal has been opened. But as yet, nothing has come through.

Keeping watch. All is not what it seems ...

PROLOGUE

All seems quiet and peaceful at Rockhead Primary ...

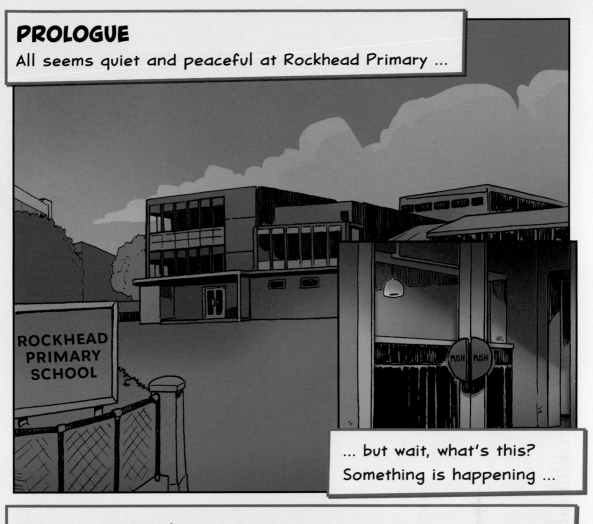

... but wait, what's this?
Something is happening ...

There are strange lights and noises ...

... and a visitor from another world is about to arrive.

BZZZZZ!

ZZZZZPPPPPTTTTT!

BZZZZZ!

But this is no intergalactic tourist ...

... and it definitely doesn't want to be seen.

CRACK!

KER-UNCH!

TINKLE!

It has an important job to do ...

... and not much time to get it done.

Librarian:
Mrs F. Cradock

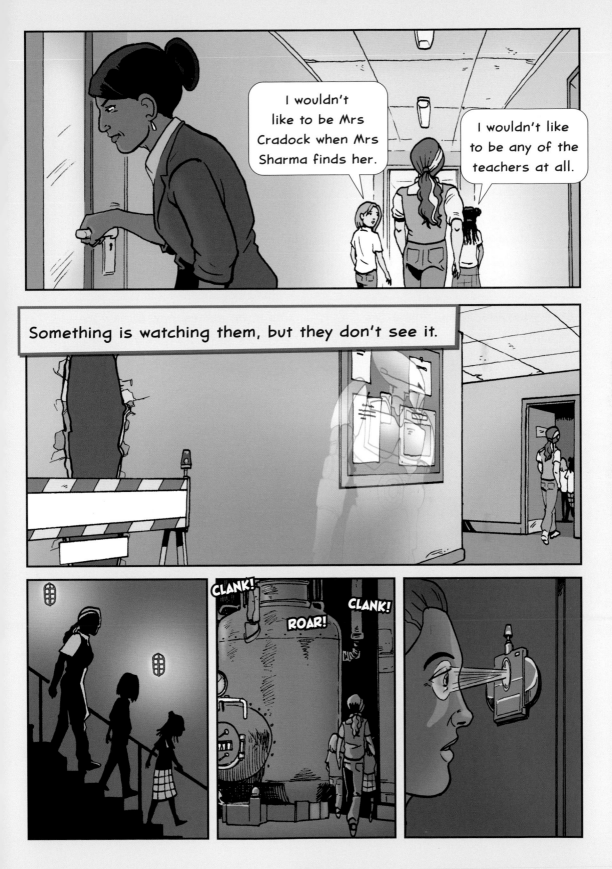

11

It's definitely an alien. The camera in the classroom got a few seconds of film before the intruder destroyed it. But as for where it is now, kids — I'm afraid we just don't know.

We've searched the whole school. But there's no sign of it anywhere.

Maybe it's got out of the school and gone somewhere else ...

Er ... I think it's in the Library.

I don't think so. We looked in there, didn't we, Ripley?

We most certainly did.

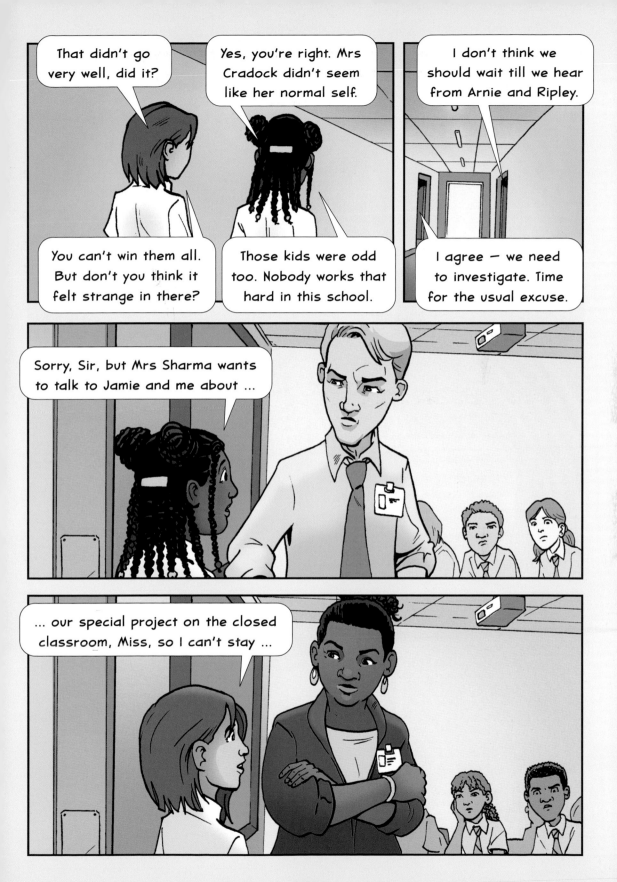

OK, so what's the plan?

We should check out the classroom. At least we know the alien was definitely there to begin with.

Wait, what's that?

What's what?

Sorry, I just had that funny feeling. You know — when you suddenly think you're being watched.

Oh yeah, I get that sometimes. Then I look around and it's usually my dad checking up on me.

Absolutely fascinating! The power surge must have been immense.

But only one intruder came through. Not much of an invasion, is it?

I don't think it's here on a friendly visit, though. It definitely didn't want us to get a look at it. And now it seems to have gone into hiding.

Maybe it's shy. Or just cunning ...

OK, what do we know so far? The intruder arrives, then strange things start happening in the Library ...

Which is where you can find out a lot of stuff. Those kids were looking at information about our planet, and our defences ...

You realise what this means? It's more than just an intruder, it's a ...

... spy!

We'd better go and tell Arnie and Ripley what we've come up with.

Hang on — what's happening there?

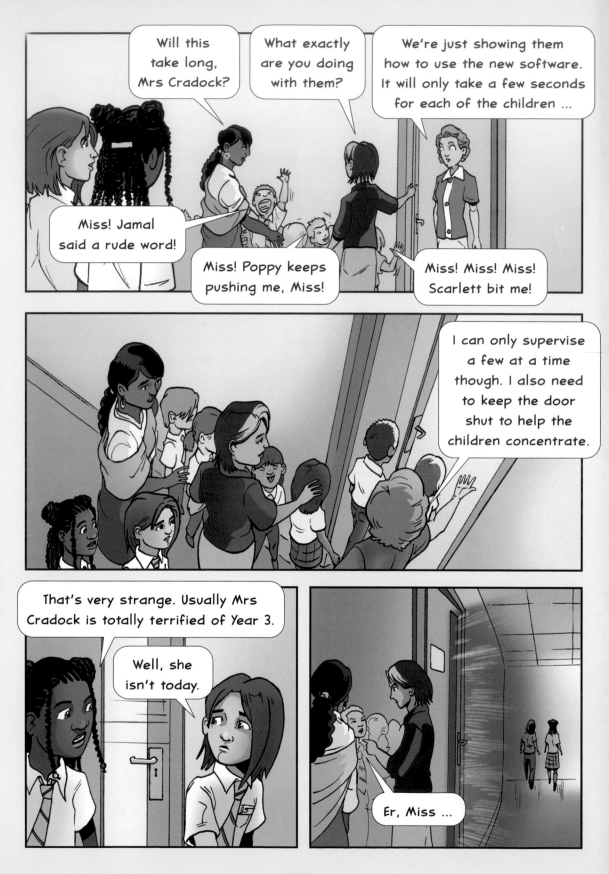

22

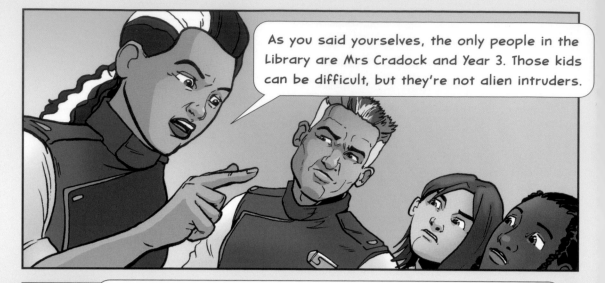

As you said yourselves, the only people in the Library are Mrs Cradock and Year 3. Those kids can be difficult, but they're not alien intruders.

Good point ... Hey, maybe the intruder is using them in some way!

But how? It doesn't seem possible.

Duh! We're talking about an alien that came out of a space portal.

It doesn't look like we can do any more for the time being. You'd better get back to class, kids. Keep your eyes peeled — we'll keep you posted!

Yeah, so it's probably using some kind of amazing alien technology.

Well, we still need to track the intruder down, whatever it's doing.

and Year 3 are behaving very strangely.

It's like wild animals, they're at their most dangerous when they're quiet.

It makes a nice change though, doesn't it? I might even make it through the day without a headache.

You'll be lucky.

Check out the faces of the Year 3s and 4s! I mean, they all look like robots. This is seriously weird.

You can say that again.

This is seriously ...

Wait, I want to hear this.

Well, I'm impressed! Some of these children are behaving really well. I asked for an improvement, and this is very encouraging. Keep up the good work, Miss Begum and Miss Sweet.

At least someone is happy.

Yes, Mrs Sharma.

Come on, let's see if Arnie and Ripley have found out anything else.

27

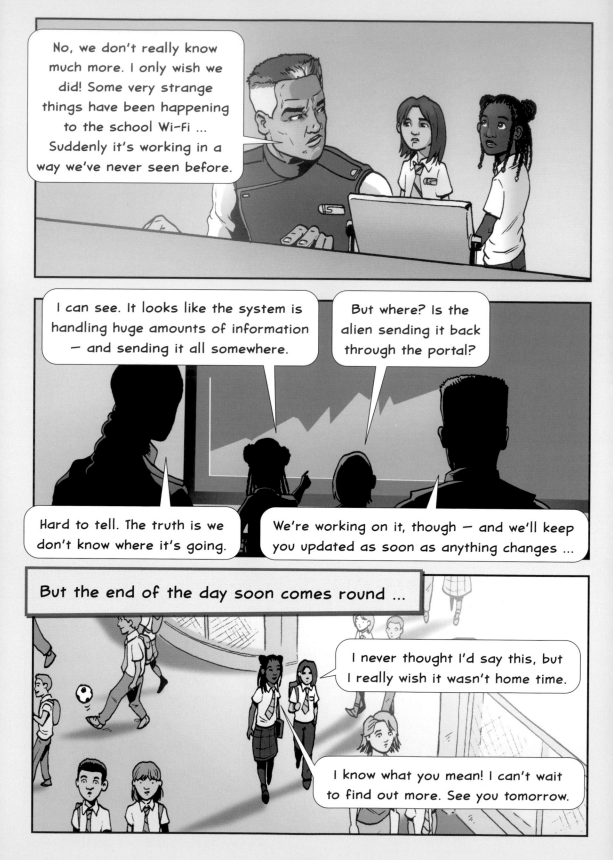

No, we don't really know much more. I only wish we did! Some very strange things have been happening to the school Wi-Fi ... Suddenly it's working in a way we've never seen before.

I can see. It looks like the system is handling huge amounts of information — and sending it all somewhere.

But where? Is the alien sending it back through the portal?

Hard to tell. The truth is we don't know where it's going.

We're working on it, though — and we'll keep you updated as soon as anything changes ...

But the end of the day soon comes round ...

I never thought I'd say this, but I really wish it wasn't home time.

I know what you mean! I can't wait to find out more. See you tomorrow.

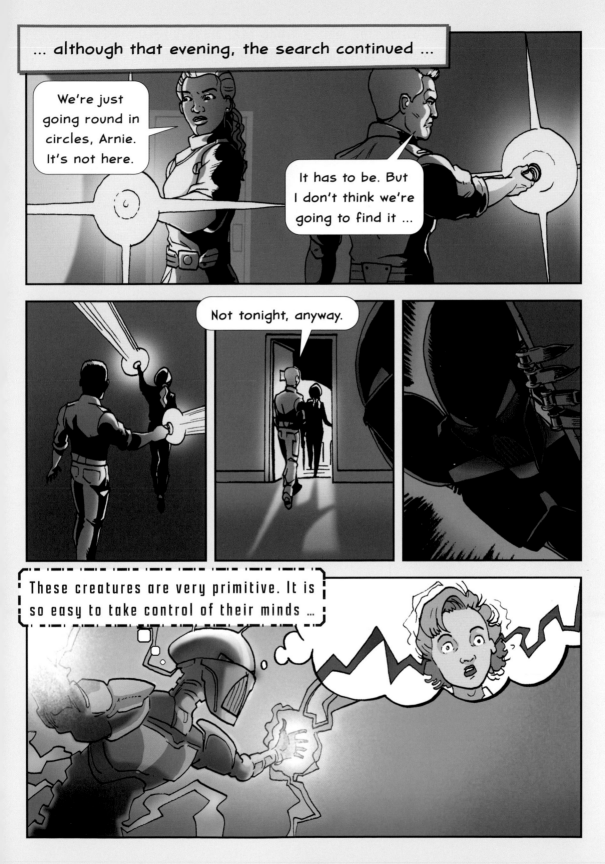

I most certainly will not. You can just turn around and take them back to ...

I can explain, Mrs Sharma. You told me to make sure the rest of the school got to use the special software. So I ordered new laptops for everyone.

I didn't give you permission to do that, did I? You should have asked me.

Don't worry, Mrs Sharma. It's a special deal for schools. If we don't like them, we can send them back before we have to pay. The mission will be complete by then.

Really? Excellent work, Mrs Cradock. I'll leave this with you, then. And I do like your idea of the school being on a mission ... a mission to improve. Carry on, everyone!

Fair enough. The intruder returned to the classroom last night and destroyed the monitoring devices. Then there was a brief power surge in the portal.

Alien presence detected!!!!

Monitoring devices destroyed!!!!;

POWER SURGE IN ALIEN PORTAL!!!!!!!!!

That would be my guess. The Wi-Fi seems to have settled down too.

So it looks like our visitor has gone back to wherever it came from.

Maybe. But it still doesn't feel right to me somehow ...

You can't leave it there, Arnie. Why are you still worried?

It's all a bit too easy. Things don't usually work out that way, at least not in my experience, but then maybe I should listen to Ripley.

That would be a first. But it would also be a very good idea.

OK, so what's the plan now?

We'll look at the data again. We'll also need to make sure Mrs Cradock and everyone else is OK. And we'll take a look at that alien software.

And don't forget, the intruder has taken back all the information it downloaded ...

So there might still be an invasion!

There might. But we've been waiting for that since the portal opened in 1983, so things haven't changed. We're Sentinels, so we're always on guard! See you later, kids ... stay safe!

So that's it, then — the excitement is over. I know I should be pleased, but I can't help feeling disappointed.

Oh well. But I would have loved to have seen the alien. Even just a glimpse ...

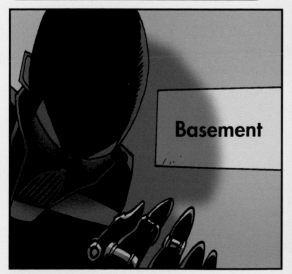

Basement

Oh, don't worry, Earthling. You will be seeing me before too long ...

Later that morning — Mrs Cradock is keeping busy.

Make sure you take them to every classroom. It is vital we get the whole school working with the software before the end of the day.

You know, I don't care what Ripley says. Even if the intruder has gone, this is all very strange.

It's more than strange. It's totally weird. We should do more investigating whether Ripley likes it or not.

Hey there, Miss Sweet and Miss Begum. Everything OK with you?

Librarian: Mrs F. Cradock

CLASS 4J – Class Teacher Mr Johnson

Everything ... is ... fine, Jamie Ballard and Verna Lee. We ... are ... Mrs Cradock's ... helpers.

Now that was creepy. It's starting to feel like we're in a horror movie.

Hold on — I've got an idea. Let's see what they're doing in here.

Where have you been, Jamie? Actually, I don't want to know. I'm just glad you've turned up at last. We're already late.

Late for what, Miss?

It's our turn to find out about this new software. Mrs Cradock says we've got to go to the Library. It won't take long.

But we can't go to the Library, Miss.

Verna's right, Sir, we have to ...

What are you talking about, Verna? Of course you can. Move along now.

Don't give us any of that 'special project' stuff, Jamie.

Sorry we're late, Mrs Cradock. How are we going to do this?

The children can line up here, and we'll take them in two at a time.

We'd rather not.

Right, that means you two are first, Jamie and Verna. In you go.

42

Are you all right, Mrs Sharma?

Mrs Sharma! I didn't hear you coming up behind us. You scared me half to death.

Tell me, children — what can you hear?

We can't hear anything.

Exactly. There's nothing to hear. No teachers shouting or children being noisy. Everybody is working quietly ... It's beautiful, isn't it? I feel my mission is accomplished ...

Er ... I suppose so.

Well, at least it looks like the alien hasn't got to Mrs Sharma yet.

Is that what you think is happening? It's taking everybody over?

I do. I think the alien took control of Mrs Cradock when she came in yesterday. Then it put something into the Library computers ...

... and it's been using them to take control of everybody else in the school! Of course, it's obvious now. But why are they looking at so much stuff on the Internet? What's that all about?

I think they're absorbing far more information than the alien could on its own. And somehow it's using our Wi-Fi to take that information from their brains and store it somewhere else.

Whoa, I get it! The alien made Mrs Cradock order those laptops so it would all be easier. Umm, maybe it's like a multi-player game, but taken to a whole new level. How cool is that ...

Er ... the door is open, Jamie. That isn't right, is it?

You two are also very clever, Verna Lee and Jamie Ballard. I have been watching you, and you are far more clever than these two adults of your species.

SPACE RADIATION LEVEL RISING — CRITICAL IN 11MIN 23SECS AND COUNTING, 11.22, 11.21, 11.20, 11.19 ...

That's good to hear. Can you say it again so I can record it and play it back to them later? I don't think they're listening right now.

Never mind all that. I've got lots of questions for you. How does the portal work? Which galaxy are you from? Is there an invasion coming? Are you ...

There is no time for questions. My mission is nearly complete. The portal will open again soon, and ...

Panel 1:

Prepare yourselves to enter the portal. It will be fully open in four of your Earth minutes.

BZZZZZTTTTT!

ZZZZZZZZPPPPTTT!

CRACKLE!

CRACKLE!

I'm just hoping it didn't come across that new software. You know, the most brilliant piece of software that's ever been developed.

Panel 2:

Tell me more of this ... software.

I should never have mentioned it. I mean, it's really brilliant and amazing. It's the key to everything! If you get hold of it we will never be able to defeat you. That's right, isn't it, Verna?

Er ... oh yes, absolutely! You should never have mentioned it, Jamie!

Panel 3:

I will download this software into my memory bank. It will complete my mission! Those who sent me will be very pleased ... See to it, Jamie Ballard.

No way! I won't betray the human race!

I should have taken over your mind too, but there is no time for that. Yet you will obey me, or I will ...

All right, calm down! There's no need to lose your temper. I'll see what I can do ...

Good riddance. I'd like to say it was nice to meet you, but it wasn't.

ZZZZZZZIIIIIIIIPPPPPPPP!!!!

That last bit was fun, though. Hang on, I think Arnie and Ripley are coming round.

Jamie? Verna? I don't remember ...

Would somebody tell me what's going on in here, please? There was a lot of noise and the whole school seemed to shake!

It's a long story, Miss, and you're probably not going to believe us.

I'll be the judge of that. Come on, I'm waiting ...

We have to tell her everything. She is the Head, after all. It's her school.

Good luck with that. You can start.

Well, it all started a long time ago ...

It's very impressive — a wonderful asset for the school. I wish I'd known about it a long time ago. It's wonderful that everyone is free again as well. Although poor Mrs Cradock will need some time off to recover. And I have to say I don't think what that alien robot did was all bad ...

So I was wondering if we could still use whatever it put in the computers. The children's behaviour was so much better yesterday, and it was wonderful to see everyone working so hard.

Sorry, Mrs Sharma. That's not going to happen. Not even for Year 3. But we can offer you something.

You can keep the laptops. I've checked with HQ and we'll pay for them.

Splendid! That's very generous of you. What did you say you were called?

The Sentinels. But we're secret, so you can't tell anybody about us. I mean seriously, you can't utter a word.

My lips are sealed. Now off you go, it's home time soon and I'm busy ...

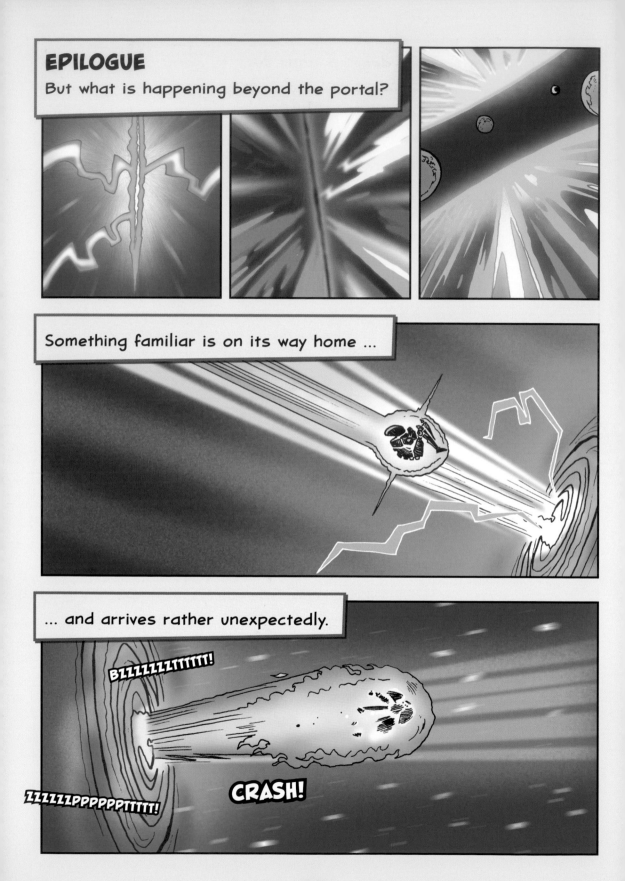

Those who sent the intruder are eager to discover whether the mission was a success ...

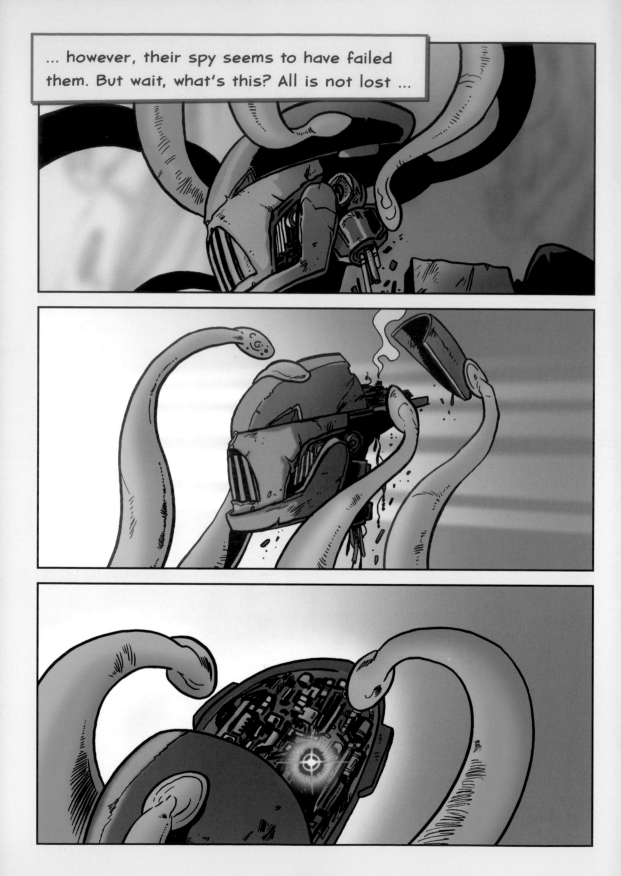

At least now they know who their enemies are ...

CHAT ABOUT THE BOOK

1 Re-read pages 53 to 55. How did Jamie and Verna trick the intruder?

2 Go to page 21. Find and copy the word that describes the power surge. What other words might the author have used?

3 Read page 30. What did the intruder mean by saying, 'two problems in particular'?

4 How did Year 3's behaviour change in the story? What did this tell Jamie and Verna?

5 Go to page 6. Why does the author only tell us a little about the visitor to Rockhead Primary School and not describe the intruder in more detail?

6 Look at page 38. Why are capital letters used for the word, 'DEFINITELY'?

7 Go to the end of the story. Do you think the danger has passed at Rockhead Primary School?

8 Do you agree that Jamie and Verna are the heroes in this story? Do you know any other stories in which children are the heroes?